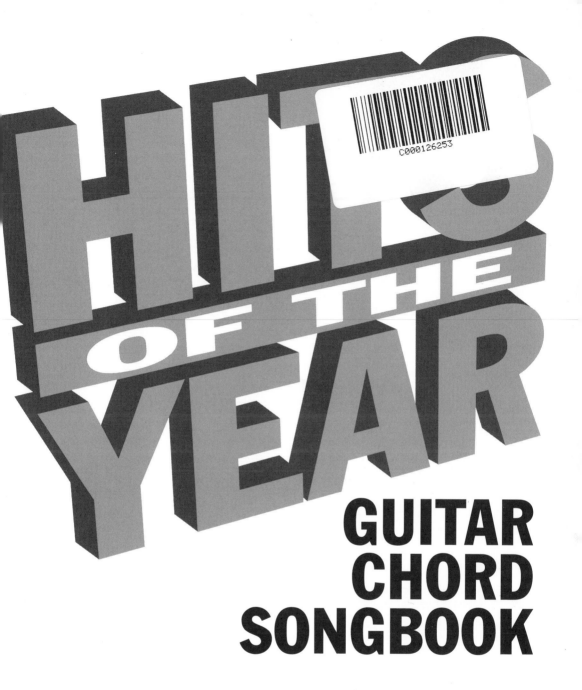

GUITAR
CHORD
SONGBOOK

WISE PUBLICATIONS
part of The Music Sales Group
London / New York / Paris / Sydney / Copenhagen /
Berlin / Madrid / Hong Kong / Tokyo

Published by
Wise Publications
14-15 Berners Street, London W1T 3LJ, UK.

Exclusive Distributors:

Music Sales Limited
Distribution Centre, Newmarket Road,
Bury St Edmunds, Suffolk IP33 3YB, UK.

Music Sales Pty Limited
4th floor, Lisgar House, 30-32 Carrington Street,
Sydney, NSW 2000, Australia.

Order No. AM1011263
ISBN: 978-1-78558-187-8
Wise Publications,
a division of Music Sales Limited.

Compiled and edited by Adrian Hopkins.
Cover design by Tim Field.
Printed in the EU.

Your Guarantee of Quality:

As publishers, we strive to produce every book
to the highest commercial standards.

This book has been carefully designed to minimise awkward
page turns and to make playing from it a real pleasure.

Particular care has been given to specifying acid-free,
neutral-sized paper made from pulps which have not been
elemental chlorine bleached. This pulp is from farmed sustainable
forests and was produced with special regard for the environment.

Throughout, the printing and binding have been planned to ensure
a sturdy, attractive publication which should give years of enjoyment.

If your copy fails to meet our high standards,
please inform us and we will gladly replace it.

www.musicsales.com

Bills

Words & Music by Jacob Hindlin, Eric Frederic,
Rickard Goransson & Gamal Lewis

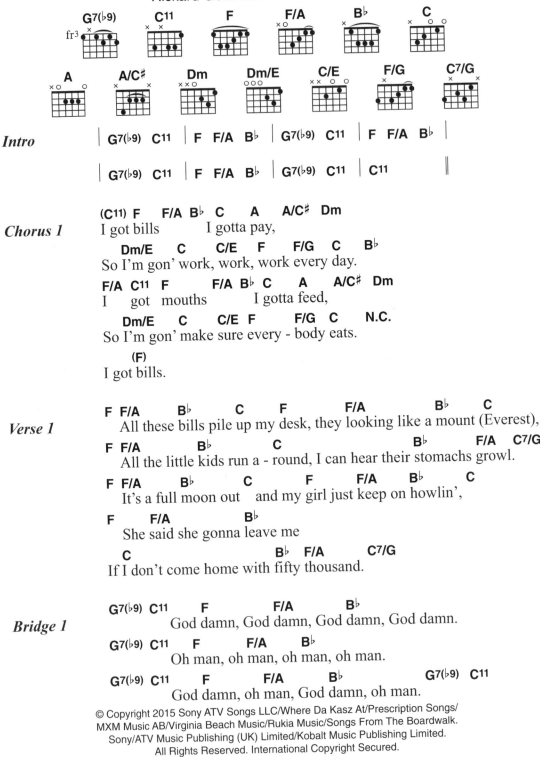

Intro

| G7(♭9) C11 | F F/A B♭ | G7(♭9) C11 | F F/A B♭ |

| G7(♭9) C11 | F F/A B♭ | G7(♭9) C11 | C11 ‖

Chorus 1

(C11) F   F/A B♭ C   A   A/C♯ Dm
I got bills   I gotta pay,

Dm/E   C   C/E F   F/G C   B♭
So I'm gon' work, work, work every day.

F/A C11 F   F/A B♭ C   A   A/C♯ Dm
I   got mouths   I gotta feed,

Dm/E   C   C/E F   F/G C   N.C.
So I'm gon' make sure every - body eats.

(F)
I got bills.

Verse 1

F F/A   B♭   C   F   F/A   B♭   C
All these bills pile up my desk, they looking like a mount (Everest),

F F/A   B♭   C   B♭   F/A C7/G
All the little kids run a - round, I can hear their stomachs growl.

F F/A   B♭   C   F   F/A   B♭   C
It's a full moon out   and my girl just keep on howlin',

F   F/A   B♭
She said she gonna leave me

C   B♭ F/A   C7/G
If I don't come home with fifty thousand.

Bridge 1

G7(♭9) C11   F   F/A   B♭
God damn, God damn, God damn, God damn.

G7(♭9) C11   F   F/A   B♭
Oh man, oh man, oh man, oh man.

G7(♭9) C11   F   F/A   B♭   G7(♭9) C11
God damn, oh man, God damn, oh man.

Chorus 2

(C11) F   F/A B♭ C   A   A/C♯ Dm
I got bills   I gotta pay,

      Dm/E   C   C/E F   F/G C   B♭
So I'm gon' work, work, work every day.

F/A C11 F   F/A B♭ C   A   A/C♯ Dm
I   got mouths   I gotta feed,

      Dm/E   C   C/E F   F/G C   B♭
So I'm gon' make sure every - body eats.

F/A C11 (F)
I   got bills.

Verse 2

F   F/A   B♭   C
  Woke up and I bumped my head,

F   F/A   B♭   C
Stubbed my toe on the edge of the bed,

F   F/A   B♭   C
Opened the fridge and the food all gone,

            B♭   F/A   C7/G
Neighbour damn dog had crapped on my lawn.

F   F/A   B♭   C
Hopped in the car and the car won't start,

  F   F/A   B♭   C
It's too damn hot but I still gotta walk,

   F   F/A   B♭   C
Be - hind an old lady in the grocery line,

          B♭   F/A   C7/G
Praying that my card don't get de - clined.

Bridge 2   As Bridge 1

Chorus 3

(C11) F   F/A B♭ C   A   A/C♯ Dm
I got bills   I gotta pay,

      Dm/E   C   C/E F   F/G C   B♭
So I'm gon' work, work, work every day.

F/A C11 F   F/A B♭ C   A   A/C♯ Dm
I   got mouths   I gotta feed,

      Dm/E   C   C/E F   F/G C   B♭
So I'm gon' make sure every - body eats.

Am Gm
I   got.

Instrumental | F F/A B♭ C | A A/C♯ Dm Dm/E | C C/E F F/G | C B♭ F/A C11 |

                   | F F/A B♭ C | A A/C♯ Dm Dm/E | C C/E F F/G | C B♭ F/A C11 ‖

Bridge 3

G7(♭9) C11   F   F/A B♭
          And my shoes,

G7(♭9) C11   F   F/A B♭
        My shoes,

        G7(♭9) C11 F F/A   B♭   G7(♭9) C11
I said my shoes   ain't got no sole._____

Chorus 4

(C11) F   F/A B♭ C   A   A/C# Dm
I got bills   I gotta pay,

   Dm/E   C   C/E   F   F/G C   B♭
So I'm gon' work, work, work every day.

F/A C/11 F   F/A B♭ C   A   A/C# Dm
I   got mouths   I gotta feed,

   Dm/E   C   C/E F   F/G C   N.C.
So I'm gon' make sure every - body eats.

Chorus 5

N.C. F   F/A B♭ C   A   A/C# Dm
I got bills   I gotta pay,

   Dm/E   C   C/E   F   F/G C   B♭
So I'm gon' work, work, work every day.

F/A C11 F   F/A B♭ C   A   A/C# Dm
I   got mouths   I gotta feed,

   Dm/E   C   C/E F   F/G C   B♭
So I'm gon' make sure every - body eats.

Am Gm (F)
I   got bills.

Outro

F F/A   B♭ C A   A/C#   Dm
   Mama got bills,   your daddy got bills,

    Dm/E   F   Gm C   B♭   F/A
Your sister got bills,   your auntie got bills.

  C7/G F
I got bills.

    F/A   B♭   C A   A/C#   Dm   Dm/E
Your uncle got bills,   every - body got bills,

 C   C/E   F   Gm C B♭ F/A C7/G F
  Every - body got bills.

Blank Space

Words & Music by Max Martin, Taylor Swift & Shellback

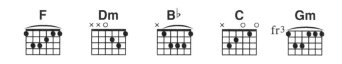

Intro | F   ‖

Verse 1
    F
    Nice to meet you, where you been?
                  Dm
I could show you incredible things,

Magic, madness, heaven, sin.

Saw you there and I thought,
B♭
Oh my God, look at that face,

You look like my next mistake.
C
Love's a game, wanna play?

Verse 2
    F
    New money, suit and tie,
                  Dm
I can read you like a maga - zine.

Ain't it funny, rumours fly
                  B♭
And I know you heard about me.

So hey, let's be friends,

I'm dying to see how this one ends.
C
Grab your passport and my hand,
N.C.
I can make the bad guys good for a weekend.

Pre-chorus 1

F
So, it's gonna be forever,

Or it's gonna go down in flames.

Dm
You can tell me when it's over,

If the high was worth the pain.

Gm
Got a long list of ex-lovers,

They'll tell you I'm insane.

B♭
'Cause you know I love the players

                        F
And you love the game.

Chorus 1

F
'Cause we're young and we're reckless,

We'll take this way too far.

Dm
It'll leave you breathless

Or with a nasty scar.

Gm
Got a long list of ex-lovers,

They'll tell you I'm insane.

B♭
But I've got a blank space, baby,

N.C.
And I'll write your name.

Verse 3

F
Cherry lips, crystal skies,

                        Dm
I could show you incredible things,

Stolen kisses, pretty lies,

                        B♭
You're the King, baby, I'm your Queen.

cont.   Find out what you want,

                 Be that girl for a month,
                 C
                 Wait, the worst is yet to come, oh no.

                        F
Verse 4   Screaming, crying, perfect storms,
                                 Dm
                 I can make all the tables turn.

                 Rose garden filled with thorns,

                 Keep you second guessing like,
                 B♭
                 Oh my God, who is she?

                 I get drunk on jealousy,
                        C
                 But you'll come back each time you leave,
                 N.C.
                 'Cause, darling, I'm a nightmare dressed like a daydream.

Pre-chorus 2   As Pre-chorus 1

Chorus 2   As Chorus 1

                 N.C. (F)
Bridge   Boys only want love if it's torture,

                 Don't say I didn't say, I didn't warn ya.

                 Boys only want love if it's torture,

                 Don't say I didn't say, I didn't warn ya.

Pre-chorus 3   As Pre-chorus 1

Chorus 3   As Chorus 1

Outro   ‖: **F**   :‖ *Repeat and fade*

9

Blame It On Me

Words & Music by Joel Pott & George Ezra Barnett

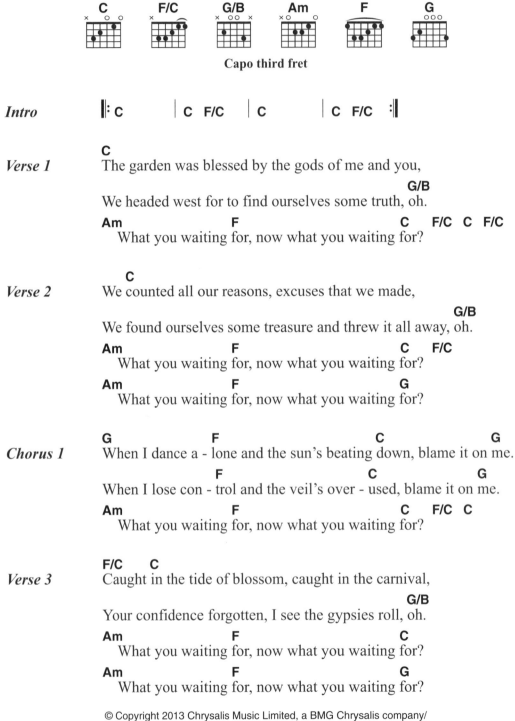

C   F/C   G/B   Am   F   G

Capo third fret

Intro   ‖: C | C F/C | C | C F/C :‖

Verse 1

C
The garden was blessed by the gods of me and you,

                                                   G/B
We headed west for to find ourselves some truth, oh.

Am   F   C   F/C C F/C
   What you waiting for, now what you waiting for?

Verse 2

    C
We counted all our reasons, excuses that we made,

                                                   G/B
We found ourselves some treasure and threw it all away, oh.

Am   F   C   F/C
   What you waiting for, now what you waiting for?

Am   F   G
   What you waiting for, now what you waiting for?

Chorus 1

G   F   C   G
When I dance a - lone and the sun's beating down, blame it on me.

                          F   C   G
When I lose con - trol and the veil's over - used, blame it on me.

Am   F   C   F/C C
   What you waiting for, now what you waiting for?

Verse 3

F/C   C
Caught in the tide of blossom, caught in the carnival,

                                               G/B
Your confidence forgotten, I see the gypsies roll, oh.

Am   F   C
   What you waiting for, now what you waiting for?

Am   F   G
   What you waiting for, now what you waiting for?

Chorus 2

G   F   C   G
When I dance a - lone, and the sun's beating down, blame it on me.

                  F   C   G
When I lose con - trol and the veil's over - used, blame it on me.

Am   F   C
What you waiting for, now what you waiting for?

Am   F   G
What you waiting for, now what you waiting for?

Chorus 3

G   F   C   G
When I dance a - lone, and the sun's beating down, blame it on me.

                  F   C   G
When I lose con - trol and the veil's over - used, blame it on me.

                  F   C   G
When I dance a - lone, I know I'll go, blame it on me, oh.

                  F   C   G
When I lose con - trol, I know I'll go, blame it on me, oh.

Outro

Am   F   C
What you waiting for, now what you waiting for?

Am   F   G
What you waiting for, now what you waiting for?

Blud

Words & Music by Bridie Monds-Watson

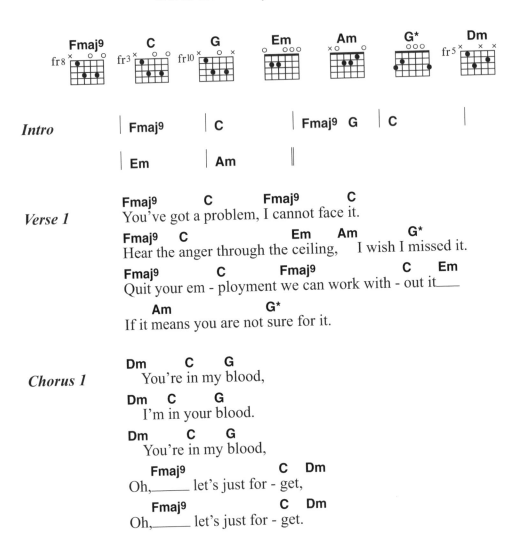

Intro | Fmaj9 | C | Fmaj9 G | C | |

| Em | Am | ||

Verse 1

Fmaj9   C   Fmaj9   C
You've got a problem, I cannot face it.

Fmaj9 C   Em Am   G*
Hear the anger through the ceiling, I wish I missed it.

Fmaj9   C   Fmaj9   C Em
Quit your em - ployment we can work with - out it___

    Am   G*
If it means you are not sure for it.

Chorus 1

Dm   C   G
  You're in my blood,

Dm C   G
  I'm in your blood.

Dm   C   G
  You're in my blood,

    Fmaj9   C Dm
Oh,___ let's just for - get,

    Fmaj9   C Dm
Oh,___ let's just for - get.

Verse 2

Fmaj9   **C**
Get up before they shoot you down,

Fmaj9   **C**
This is not worth the risk.

      Fmaj9   **C**
The shouting, dampened by the ceiling,

Em   **Am**   **G**
Oh, and I am waiting for what this is, oh, oh.

Chorus 2

Dm   **C**   **G**
   You're in my blood,

Dm   **C**   **G**
  I'm in your blood.

Dm   **C**   **G**
   You're in my blood,

    Fmaj9   **C**   **Dm**
Oh,_____ let's just for - get,

    Fmaj9   **C**
Oh,_____ let's just for - get.

Can't Feel My Face

Words & Music by Savan Kotecha, Max Martin,
Peter Svensson, Ali Payami & Abel Tesfaye

G   F   Am

Intro | G | F | Am | Am ||

Verse 1

            G   F

And I know she'll be the death of me, at least we'll both be numb,

            Am

And she'll always get the best of me, the worst is yet to come.

            G   F

But at least we'll both be beautiful and stay forever young,

            Am

This I know, yeah, this I know.

Pre-chorus 1

   (Am)   G   F

She told me, don't worry a - bout it,

                     Am

She told me, don't worry no more.

                     G   F

We both know we can't go with - out it,

                    Am

She told me you'll never be alone, oh-oh, whoo.

Chorus 1

     G   F

I can't feel my face when I'm with you,

           Am

But I love it, but I love it, oh.

     G   F

I can't feel my face when I'm with you,

           Am

But I love it, but I love it, oh.

14

Verse 2
               G   F

And I know she'll be the death of me, at least we'll both be numb,

           Am

And she'll always get the best of me, the worst is yet to come.

       G   F

All the misery was necessary when we're deep in love,

           Am

Yes I know, yes I know, man, I know.

Pre-chorus 2   As Pre-chorus 1

Chorus 2   As Chorus 1

Chorus 3   As Chorus 1

Link | G | F | Am | Am   ‖

Pre-chorus 3   As Pre-chorus 1

Chorus 4   As Chorus 1

Chorus 5   As Chorus 1

Outro | G | F | Am | Am   ‖

Cheerleader

Words & Music by Clifton Dillon, Sly Dunbar,
Mark Antonio Bradford, Omar Samuel Pasely & Ryan Dillon

E   B   A

Intro

| E | B A | E | B A |

| E | B A | E | B A ‖

Verse 1

(A)   E   B   A   E
When I need motivation,   my one so - lution is my queen,

                   B   A
'Cause she stays strong,   yeah, yeah.

       E   B   A
She is always in my corner right there when I want her,

       E   B   A
All these other girls are tempting, but I'm empty when you're gone

And they say,

Pre-chorus 1

E   A   B   A
   Do you need me, do you think I'm pretty,

      E   A   B   A
Do I make you feel like cheating? I'm like no, not really 'cause

Chorus 1

E   A   B   A
Oh, I think that I've found myself a cheerleader,

E   A   B   A
   She is always right there when I need her.

E   A   B   A
Oh, I think that I've found myself a cheerleader,

E   A   B   A
   She is always right there when I need her.

Verse 2

```
(A) E            A     B          A
She walks like a model   she grants my wishes
      E       A     B          A
Like a genie in a bottle,    yeah, yeah.
             E         A       B           A
'Cause I'm the wizard of love and I got the magic wand,
          E          A              B              A
All these other girls are tempting, but I'm empty when you're gone

And they say,
```

Pre-chorus 2   As Pre-chorus 1

Chorus 2   As Chorus 1

Instrumental
```
| E  A    | B  A    | E  A    | B  A    |

| E  A    | B  A    | E  A    | B  A    |

| E       | B  A    | E       | B  A    |

| E       | B  A    | E       | B  A    ‖
```

Verse 3
```
(A)        E         A     B          A
She gives me love and af - fection, baby, did I mention
E             A           B          A
You're the only girl for me, no, I don't need a next one.
E             A            B              A
Mama loves you too, she thinks I made the right se - lection,
       E           A         B          A
Now all that's left to do is just for me to pop the question.
```

Chorus 3   As Chorus 1

Outro
```
| E  A    | B  A    | E  A    | B  A    |

| E  A    | B  A    | E  A    | B  A    |

| E       | B  A    ‖
```

17

Cool For The Summer

Words & Music by Savan Kotecha, Max Martin,
Alexander Kronlund, Demi Lovato & Ali Payami

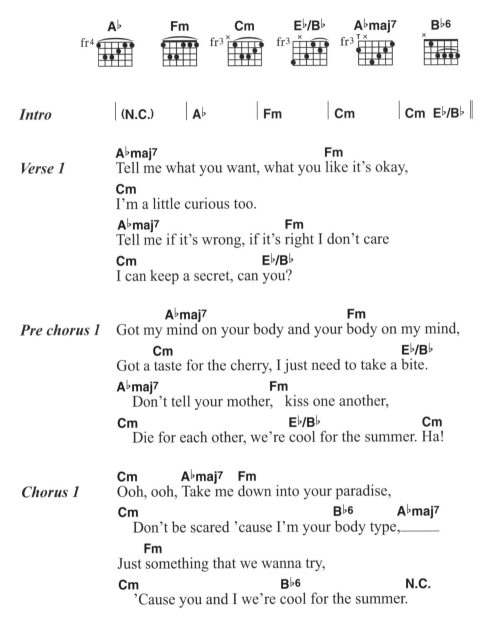

Intro | (N.C.) | A♭ | Fm | Cm | Cm E♭/B♭ ‖

Verse 1

A♭maj7   Fm
Tell me what you want, what you like it's okay,

Cm
I'm a little curious too.

A♭maj7   Fm
Tell me if it's wrong, if it's right I don't care

Cm   E♭/B♭
I can keep a secret, can you?

Pre chorus 1

A♭maj7   Fm
Got my mind on your body and your body on my mind,

          Cm   E♭/B♭
Got a taste for the cherry, I just need to take a bite.

A♭maj7   Fm
   Don't tell your mother,   kiss one another,

Cm   E♭/B♭   Cm
   Die for each other, we're cool for the summer. Ha!

Chorus 1

Cm   A♭maj7 Fm
Ooh, ooh, Take me down into your paradise,

Cm   B♭6   A♭maj7
   Don't be scared 'cause I'm your body type,_____

      Fm
Just something that we wanna try,

Cm   B♭6   N.C.
   'Cause you and I we're cool for the summer.

Verse 2

A♭maj7   Fm
Tell me if I won, if I did, what's my prize?
Cm   E♭/B♭
I just wanna play with you, too.
A♭maj7   Fm
Even if they judge, fuck it, I'll do the time,
N.C.   Cm   E♭/B♭
I just wanna have some fun__ with you.

Pre chorus 2   As Pre Chorus 1

Chorus 2

Cm   A♭maj7 Fm
Ooh, ooh, Take me down into your paradise,
Cm   B♭6   A♭maj7
    Don't be scared 'cause I'm your body type,_____
    Fm
Just something that we wanna try,
Cm   B♭6
   'Cause you and I we're cool for the summer.
A♭maj7 Fm
Ha!   We're cool for the summer,
Cm   E♭/B♭
   We're cool for the summer.

Link 1 | N.C. | A♭ | Fm | Cm | Cm E♭/B♭ ‖

Bridge

     A♭   Fm   Cm E♭/B♭
Got my mind on your body and your body on my mind,
        A♭   Fm   Cm E♭/B♭
Got a taste for the cherry, I just need to take a bite.
N.C.
   Take me down!

Chorus 3

A♭maj7 Fm
Take me down into your paradise,
Cm   B♭6   A♭maj7
    Don't be scared 'cause I'm your body type,_____
    Fm
Just something that we wanna try,
Cm   B♭6
   'Cause you and I we're cool for the summer.

Chorus 4

A♭maj⁷   **Fm**
Take me down, we're cool for the summer,

Cm   **B♭6**   **A♭maj⁷**
Don't be scared 'cause I'm your body type,_____

      Fm
Just something that we wanna try,

Cm   **B♭6**
  'Cause you and I we're cool for the summer.

Cm
Ha! Ooh, we're cool for the summer.

FourFiveSeconds

Words & Music by Rihanna, Paul McCartney & Kanye West

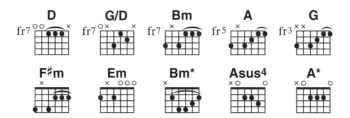

⑥ = D   ③ = G
⑤ = A   ② = B
④ = D   ① = E

Verse 1

D   G/D   A   G
I think I've had enough,   I might get a little drunk.

D   G/D   Bm A   D
I say what's on my mind,   I might do a little time.

D   G/D   Bm   A
'Cause all of my kindness   is taken for weakness.

Chorus 1

(G)   D   G/D
Now I'm four, five seconds from wildin',

                     D
And we got three more days till Friday.

                                      G/D
I'm just trying to make it back home by Monday morning,

Bm   A
I swear I wish somebody would tell me ooh, that's all I want.

Verse 2

D   G/D   D   G
Woke up an optimist,   sun was shining, I'm positive.

D   G/D
Then I heard you was talking trash,

D   G/D
Hold me back, I'm 'bout to spaz.

Chorus 2

(G)   D   G/D

Yeah I'm 'bout four, five seconds from wildin',

           D

And we got three more days till Friday.

                      G/D

I'm trying to make it back home by Monday morning,

    Bm   A

I swear I wish somebody would drive me,

Ooh, that's all I want.

Bridge

G   F♯m

    And I know____ that you're out tonight,

Em

Thinking, how could I be so selfish?

G   F♯m   Em   Bm*

    But you called 'bout a thousand times,

Asus4   A*

    Wondering where I've been.____

G   F♯m

    Now, I know____ that you're out tonight,

        Em

Thinking, how could I be so reckless?

G   F♯m   Em   Bm*

    But I just can't apolo - gise,

    Asus4   A*

I hope you can under - stand.

Verse 3

   D   G/D   Bm   A

    If I go to jail tonight,   promise you'll pay my bail.

   D   G/D

    See they want to buy my pride,

  Bm   A   D

    But that just ain't up for sale.

              G/D   Bm   A

See all of my kindness   is taken for weakness.

Chorus 3   As Chorus 1

Chorus 4
     D   G/D

Four, five seconds from wildin',

                   D

And we got three more days till Friday.

                                        G/D

Just trying to make it back home by Monday morning,

  Bm   A

I swear I wish somebody would tell me,

'Cause that's all I want.

Drag Me Down

Words & Music by John Ryan, Jamie Scott & Julian Bunetta

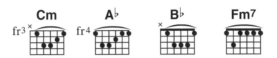

Verse 1

Cm   A♭
I've got fire for a heart,
      B♭
I'm not scared of the dark,
       Fm⁷
You've never seen it look so easy.
Cm   A♭
I got a river for a soul,
      B♭
And baby you're a boat,
     Fm⁷
Baby you're my only reason.

Verse 2

    Cm   A♭
If I didn't have you there would be nothing left,
   B♭   Fm⁷
The shell of a man who could never be his best.
    Cm   A♭
If I didn't have you, I'd never see the sun,
   B♭   Fm⁷
You taught me how to be someone, yeah.

Pre-chorus 1

Cm   A♭
All my life you stood by me,
B♭   Fm⁷
 When no one else was ever behind me.
Cm   A♭
All these lights, they can't blind me,
B♭   Fm⁷   (Cm)
 With your love, no - body can drag me (down.)
Cm   A♭
All my life you stood by me,
B♭   Fm⁷
 When no one else was ever behind me.

cont.

Cm   A♭
All these lights,   they can't blind me,

B♭   Fm⁷   Cm
   With your love, no - body can drag me down.

Chorus 1

Cm A♭   B♭
      Nobody, no - body,

     Fm⁷   Cm   A♭
No - body can drag me   down.

               B♭
Nobody, no - body,

     Fm⁷   Cm
No - body can drag me down.

Verse 3   As Verse 1

Verse 4   As Verse 2

Pre-chorus 2

Cm   A♭
All my life   you stood by me,

B♭   Fm⁷
   When no one else was ever behind me.

Cm   A♭
All these lights,   they can't blind me,

B♭   Fm⁷   Cm
   With your love, no - body can drag me down.

Chorus 2

Cm A♭   B♭
      Nobody, no - body,

     Fm⁷   Cm   A♭
No - body can drag me   down.

             B♭
Nobody, no - body,

     Fm⁷
No - body can drag me.

Pre-chorus 3   As Pre-chorus 1

Chorus 3   As Chorus 1

Chorus 4   As Chorus 1

Elastic Heart

Words & Music by Sia Furler, Thomas Pentz, Abel Tesfaye & Andrew Swanson

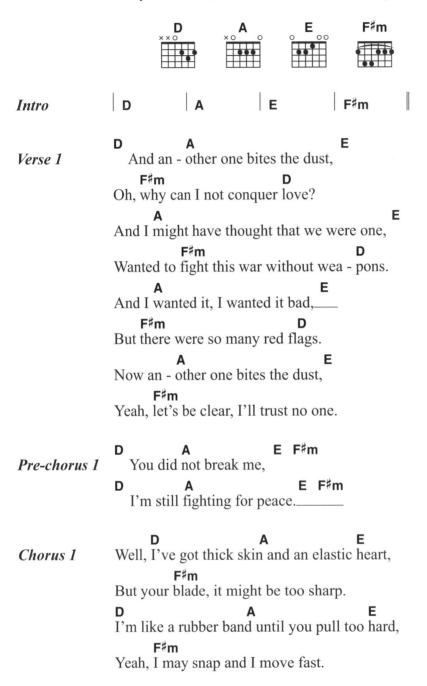

Intro | D | A | E | F#m ||

Verse 1

D   A   E
And an - other one bites the dust,

F#m   D
Oh, why can I not conquer love?

A   E
And I might have thought that we were one,

F#m   D
Wanted to fight this war without wea - pons.

A   E
And I wanted it, I wanted it bad,___

F#m   D
But there were so many red flags.

A   E
Now an - other one bites the dust,

F#m
Yeah, let's be clear, I'll trust no one.

Pre-chorus 1

D   A   E F#m
You did not break me,

D   A   E F#m
I'm still fighting for peace.___

Chorus 1

D   A   E
Well, I've got thick skin and an elastic heart,

F#m
But your blade, it might be too sharp.

D   A   E
I'm like a rubber band until you pull too hard,

F#m
Yeah, I may snap and I move fast.

cont.

      D   A   E   F♯m
But you won't see me fall a - part,_____

      D   A   F♯m
'Cause I've got an e - lastic heart._____

Link 1

      D   A   E   F♯m
I've got an e - lastic heart,

         D   A   E   F♯m
Yeah, I've got an e - lastic heart.

Verse 2

      D   A   E
And I will stay up through the night,

        F♯m   D
And let's be clear, won't close my eyes.

      A   E
And I know that I can sur - vive,

        F♯m   D
I'll walk through fire to save my life.

       A   E
And I want it, I want my life so bad,___

        F♯m   D
I'm doing everything I can.___

         A   E
Then an - other one bites the dust,

        F♯m
It's hard to lose a chosen one.

Pre-chorus 2   As Pre-Chorus 1

Chorus 2   As Chorus 1

Bridge

      D   A   E   F♯m
Oh, oh-oh-oh-oh, oh, oh, oh, oh, oh, oh-oh-oh-oh,

      D   A   E   F♯m
Oh, oh-oh-oh-oh, oh, oh, oh, oh, oh, oh-oh-oh-oh,

Chorus 3   As Chorus 1

Chorus 4   As Chorus 1

Outro

      D   A   E
I've got an e - lastic heart.

Flashlight

Words & Music by Jason Moore, Sia Furler,
Sam Smith, Christian Guzman & Mario Mejia

B♭   C   F   Dm

Intro | B♭ | C | F | B♭   ‖

Verse 1

B♭
When tomorrow comes I'll be on my own,
C   F
Feeling frightened of the things that I don't know.
                                    B♭
When tomorrow comes, tomorrow comes, tomorrow comes.
Dm
And though the road is long, I look up to the sky,
C   F
And in the dark I found, lost hope that I won't fly.
                                B♭
And I sing along, I sing a - long, and I sing along.

Chorus 1

F
I got all I need when I got you and I,
C   Dm
I look around me and see a sweet life.___

I'm stuck in the dark but you're my flashlight,
B♭   F
You're getting me, getting me through the night.___

Kickstart my heart when you shine it in my eyes,   C
Can't lie, it's a sweet life.   Dm

Stuck in the dark but you're my flashlight,
B♭
You're getting me, getting me through the night.

Link 1

      F   **C**
    'Cause you're my flash - light,

                    Dm   **B♭**
You're my flash - light, you're my flash - light, oh.

Verse 2

    Dm
    I see the shadows long beneath the mountain top,

    C   **F**
    I'm not afraid when the rain won't stop,

                             B♭
'Cause you light the way, you light the way, you light the way.

Chorus 2   As Chorus 1

Bridge

    Dm   **C**   **B♭**
(Light, light, light, you're my flash - light)

                        C   **Dm**
Light, light, you're my flash - light.

                  C   **B♭**
Light, light, light, light, oh,___

You're my flash, oh.

Chorus 3   As Chorus 1

Link 2

    F   **C**
    'Cause you're my flash - light,

                          Dm
'Cause you're my flash - light,

               B♭
You're my flash - light.

F   **C**
Ooh, ooh, ooh, ooh,

Dm   **B♭**
Ooh,_____ oh, oh-oh.

Outro

(B♭)   **F**
You're my flash - light, light, light,

                    C   **Dm**
You're my flash - light, light, light, yeah, yeah.

                                B♭
(Light, light, light, you're my flash - light, light, light.)

                    F
You're my flash - light.

High By The Beach

Words & Music by Lana Del Rey

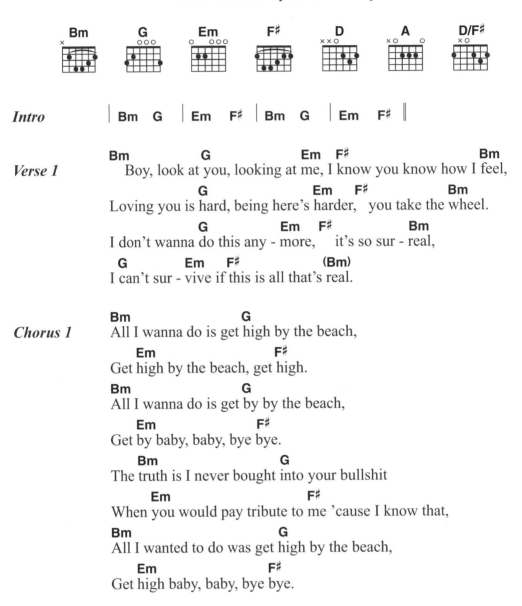

Intro | Bm G | Em F♯ | Bm G | Em F♯ |

Verse 1

Bm   G   Em F♯   Bm
Boy, look at you, looking at me, I know you know how I feel,
       G   Em F♯   Bm
Loving you is hard, being here's harder, you take the wheel.
       G   Em F♯   Bm
I don't wanna do this any - more, it's so sur - real,
   G   Em F♯   (Bm)
I can't sur - vive if this is all that's real.

Chorus 1

Bm   G
All I wanna do is get high by the beach,
 Em   F♯
Get high by the beach, get high.
Bm   G
All I wanna do is get by by the beach,
 Em   F♯
Get by baby, baby, bye bye.
  Bm   G
The truth is I never bought into your bullshit
  Em   F♯
When you would pay tribute to me 'cause I know that,
Bm   G
All I wanted to do was get high by the beach,
 Em   F♯
Get high baby, baby, bye bye.

Verse 2

    Bm   G   Em F♯   Bm
      Boy, look at you looking at me, I know you don't under - stand,

                    G   Em   F♯   Bm
     You could be a bad mother - fucker but that don't make you a man.

                  G   Em
     Now you're just an - other one of my problems,

       F♯   Bm
     Be - cause you got out of hand,

       G   Em   F♯
     We won't sur - vive, we're sinking into the sand.

Chorus 2   As Chorus 1

Middle

     G   D
     Lights, camera, acción; I'll do it on my own,

     A   Em   D/F♯
      Don't need your money, money to get me what I want.

     G   D
     Lights, camera, acción; I'll do it on my own,

     A   Em   D/F♯
      Don't need your money, money to get me what I want.

Chorus 3   As Chorus 1

Bridge

‖: Bm G   Em F♯ Bm G   Em F♯   :‖
   High,_____   high,_____

Outro
(spoken)

     Bm   G   Em   F♯
      Anyone can start again, not through love, but through revenge.

     Bm   G
     Through the fire we're born again,

     Em   F♯   Bm
     Peace by vengeance brings the end. (High.___)

Hold Back The River

Words & Music by Iain Archer & James Bay

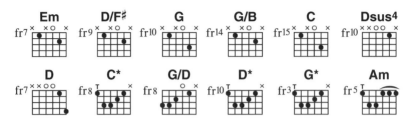

To match original recording, tune guitar down a tone
(some chords names have been simplified)

Intro | Em D/F♯ | G G/B | C G/B | G G/B |

| C G/B | G | Dsus4 | D ||

Verse 1
Em   D/F♯ G   G/B C   G/B G
Tried to   keep you close to   me,
G/B C G/B G   Dsus4 D
But life got   in between.
Em   D/F♯ G   G/B C G/B G
Tried to   square not be - ing   there,
G/B C   G/B G   Dsus4   D
But think that I should've   been.

Chorus 1
C
Hold back the river, let me look in your eyes,

Hold back the river, so I
G/D
Can stop for a minute and see where you hide,

Hold back the river, hold back.

Link 1 | Em D/F♯ | G ||

© Copyright 2014 Kobalt Music Services Limited/B Unique Music.
Kobalt Music Publishing Limited.
All Rights Reserved. International Copyright Secured.

32

Verse 2

Em   D/F♯ G G/B C   G/B G
Once up - on a   diffe - rent life,

G/B C   G/B G   Dsus4 D
We   rode our bikes into the sky.

        Em D/F♯ G   G/B C   G/B G
But now we're caught a - gainst the tide,

G/B   C   G/B G   Dsus4 D
Those dis - tant days all flashing by.

Chorus 2

C*
Hold back the river, let me look in your eyes,

Hold back the river, so I

     G/D
Can stop for a minute and be by your side,

               D*
Hold back the river, hold back.

C*
Hold back the river, let me look in your eyes,

Hold back the river, so I

     G/D
Can stop for a minute and see where you hide,

               D*
Hold back the river, hold back.

Link 2

Em D/F♯ G G/B C   G/B G
Oh, oh - ho, oh - ho, oh - oh,

G/B C G/B G   Dsus4 D
Oh - ho, oh - oh, ooh-oh, ooh-oh-oh.

Bridge 1

G*
Lonely water, lonely water,

            C*   Am
Won't you let us wander, let us hold each other.

G*
Lonely water, lonely water,

            C*   Am
Won't you let us wander, let us hold each other.

Chorus 3

C*
Hold back the river, let me look in your eyes,

Hold back the river, so I
    G/D
Can stop for a minute and be by your side,
           D*
Hold back the river, hold back.
C*
Hold back the river, let me look in your eyes,

Hold back the river, so I
    G/D
Can stop for a minute and be by your side,
           D*
Hold back the river, hold.

Bridge 2

G*
Lonely water, lonely water,
         C   Am   D*
Won't you let us wander, let us hold each other.
G*
Lonely water, lonely water,
         C   Am
Won't you let us wander, let us hold each other.

Outro

| Em D/F♯ | G G/B | C G/B | G G/B |

| C G/B | G | Dsus⁴ ‖

Hold My Hand

Words & Music by Ina Wroldsen, Jack Patterson, Jess Glynne & Janee Bennett

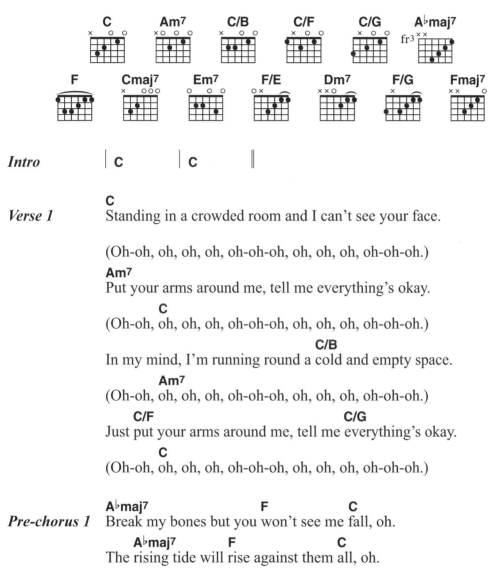

Intro | C | C ||

Verse 1

C
Standing in a crowded room and I can't see your face.

(Oh-oh, oh, oh, oh, oh-oh-oh, oh, oh, oh, oh-oh-oh.)
Am⁷
Put your arms around me, tell me everything's okay.
           C
(Oh-oh, oh, oh, oh, oh-oh-oh, oh, oh, oh, oh-oh-oh.)
                                    C/B
In my mind, I'm running round a cold and empty space.
           Am⁷
(Oh-oh, oh, oh, oh, oh-oh-oh, oh, oh, oh, oh-oh-oh.)
           C/F   C/G
Just put your arms around me, tell me everything's okay.
           C
(Oh-oh, oh, oh, oh, oh-oh-oh, oh, oh, oh, oh-oh-oh.)

Pre-chorus 1

A♭maj⁷   F   C
Break my bones but you won't see me fall, oh.
           A♭maj⁷   F   C
The rising tide will rise against them all, oh.

Chorus 1

   (C)   **Cmaj7**
Darling, hold my hand,

               Em7
Oh, won't you hold my hand?

               F   **F/E**
'Cause I don't wanna walk on my own any - more,

        Dm7
Won't you under - stand?

'Cause I don't wanna walk alone.

C   **C/B**
  I'm ready for this, there's no denying,

Am7
  I'm ready for this, you stop me falling.

F   **F/E**
  I'm ready for this, I need you all in,

Dm7   **F/G**
  I'm ready for this, so darling, hold my hand.

Verse 2

C   **C/B**
Soul is like a melting pot when you're not next to me,

     Am7
(Oh-oh, oh, oh, oh, oh-oh-oh, oh, oh, oh, oh-oh-oh.)

C/F   **C/G**
Tell me that you've got me and you're never gonna leave.

     C
(Oh-oh, oh, oh, oh, oh-oh-oh, oh, oh, oh, oh-oh-oh.)

        C/B
Trying to find a moment where I can find release.

     Am7
(Oh-oh, oh, oh, oh, oh-oh-oh, oh, oh, oh, oh-oh-oh.)

     C/F   **C/G**
Please tell me that you've got me and you're never gonna leave.

     C
(Oh-oh, oh, oh, oh, oh-oh-oh, oh, oh, oh, oh-oh-oh.)

Pre-chorus 2   As Pre-chorus 1

Chorus 2   As Chorus 1

Bridge

(F/G) **Fmaj7**   **Am7**
Don't wanna know that feeling when I'm all alone,

                              Fmaj7   **C/G**   **Dm7**
So please don't make me wait, 'cause I don't wanna break

     C   **G**
No I don't wanna fall.

                    Fmaj7   **Am7**
When you're next to me, can tell I'm not a - fraid to be,

                    Fmaj7   **C/G**   **Dm7**
That you don't make me wait and never let me break,

          C   **G**
You never let me fall.

Chorus 3

(G)   **Cmaj7**
Darling, hold my hand,

                    Em7
Oh, won't you hold my hand?

                    Dm7   **Em7**
'Cause I don't wanna walk on my own any - more,

              F
Won't you under - stand?

          N.C.
'Cause I don't wanna walk alone.

C   **C/B**
    I'm ready for this, there's no denying,

Am7
    I'm ready for this, you stop me falling.

F   **F/E**
    I'm ready for this, I need you all in,

Dm7   **F/G**   **N.C. (C)**
    I'm ready for this, so darling, won't you hold my hand.

I Really Like You

Words & Music by Peter Svensson, Carly Rae Jepsen & Jacob Hindlin

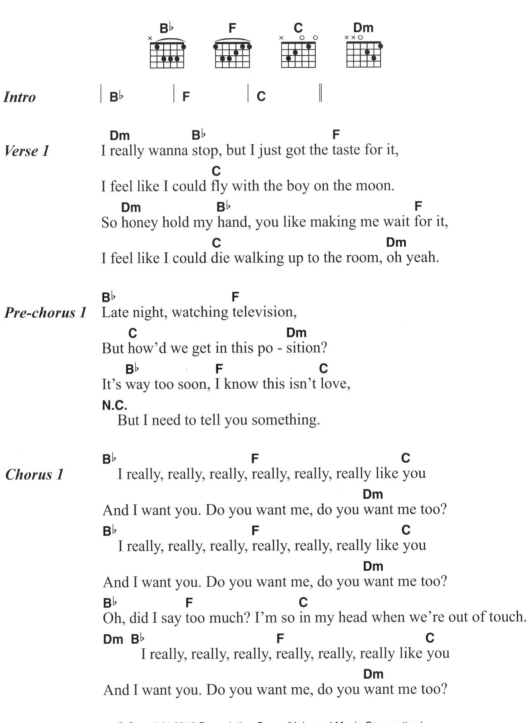

Intro | B♭ | F | C ‖

Verse 1

Dm   B♭   F
I really wanna stop, but I just got the taste for it,
                      C
I feel like I could fly with the boy on the moon.
Dm   B♭   F
So honey hold my hand, you like making me wait for it,
                    C   Dm
I feel like I could die walking up to the room, oh yeah.

Pre-chorus 1

B♭   F
Late night, watching television,
       C   Dm
But how'd we get in this po - sition?
       B♭   F   C
It's way too soon, I know this isn't love,
N.C.
But I need to tell you something.

Chorus 1

B♭   F   C
I really, really, really, really, really, really like you
                                    Dm
And I want you. Do you want me, do you want me too?
B♭   F   C
I really, really, really, really, really, really like you
                                    Dm
And I want you. Do you want me, do you want me too?
B♭   F   C
Oh, did I say too much? I'm so in my head when we're out of touch.
Dm B♭   F   C
I really, really, really, really, really, really like you
                                    Dm
And I want you. Do you want me, do you want me too?

Verse 2

N.C.   B♭   F
It's like everything you say is a sweet reve - lation,

                C
All I wanna do is get into your head.

       Dm   B♭   F
Yeah, we could stay a - lone, you and me, in this temp - tation,

                 C   Dm
Sipping on your lips, hanging on by a thread, baby.

Pre-chorus 2   As Pre-chorus 1

Chorus 2   As Chorus 1

Bridge

B♭   F
  Who gave you eyes like that,   said you could keep them?

C   Dm
  I don't know how to act or if I should be leaving.

B♭   F
  I'm running out of time,   going out of my mind,

C   N.C.
  I need to tell you something,   yeah, I need to tell you something.

Chorus 3

N.C.   B♭   F   C
Yeah.___ I really, really, really, really, really, really like you

                                      Dm
And I want you. Do you want me, do you want me too?

B♭   F   C
I really, really, really, really, really, really like you

                                      Dm
And I want you. Do you want me, do you want me too?

B♭   F   C
Oh, did I say too much? I'm so in my head when we're out of touch.

Dm B♭   F   C
   I really, really, really, really, really, really like you

                                      Dm
And I want you. Do you want me, do you want me too?

Chorus 4

B♭   F   C
Yeah. I really, really, really, really, really, really like you

                                      Dm
And I want you. Do you want me, do you want me too?

B♭   F   C
I really, really, really, really, really, really like you

                                      Dm
And I want you. Do you want me, do you want me too?

Lay Me Down

Words & Music by James Napier, Sam Smith & Elvin Smith

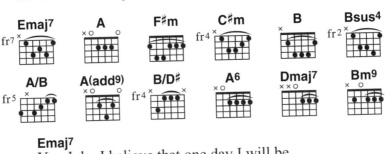

Verse 1

Emaj⁷
Yes, I do, I believe that one day I will be

                                  A
Where I was right there, right next to you.____

And it's hard, the days just seem so dark,

The moon and the stars are nothing without you.

Verse 2

Emaj⁷
Your touch, your skin, where do I begin?

                                  A
No words can explain the way I'm missing you.____

Deny this emptiness, this hole that I'm inside

These tears they tell their own story.

Pre-chorus 1

F♯m   A   C♯m B
Told me not to cry when you were gone,

         F♯m   A   Bsus⁴ A/B
But the feeling's over - whelming, it's much too____ strong.

Chorus 1

          E   C♯m
Can I lay by your side,

         F♯m A
Next to you, you

          E   C♯m
And make sure you're all right?

          F♯m
I'll take care of you,

A   A/B   E
I don't want to be here if I can't be with you   tonight.

Verse 3

        Emaj7
I'm reaching out to you,

                    A(add9)
Can you hear my_____ call?

        Emaj7
This hurt that I've been through,

                              A(add9)   **A/B**
I'm missing you, I'm missing you like   crazy, you.

Chorus 2

          E   **B/D♯ C♯m**
Can I lay by your side,

           F♯m   **A**
Next to you, to you

          E   **B/D♯** **C♯m**
And make sure you're   all right?

                  F♯m
I'll take care of you,

    A   **A/B**   **F♯m**   **A6** **Dmaj7**
I don't want to be here if I can't be with you   tonight._____

Bridge

Bm9 **F♯m**   **A6**   **Dmaj7** **Bm9**
   Oh, lay me down to - night,

F♯m   **A6**   **Dmaj7** **Bm9**
Lay me by your side.

       F♯m   **A6**   **Dmaj7** **Bm9**
Whoa, lay me down to - night,_____

F♯m   **A6**   **A/B**
Lay me by your side.

Outro

          E   **C♯m**
Can I lay by your side,

           F♯m A   **A/B E**
Next to you, you?_____

Lips Are Movin'

Words & Music by Kevin Kadish & Meghan Trainor

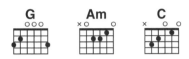

G	Am	C

                 G   Am   C

Pre-chorus 1   If your lips are moving,   if your lips are moving,

                                                   G

If your lips are moving, then you're lying, lying, lying, babe.

                                   Am   C

If your lips are moving,   if your lips are moving,

                                                 G

If your lips are moving then you're lying, lying, lying, babe.

                 G

Verse 1   Boy, look at me in my face,

                 Am

Tell me that you're not just about this bass.

                 C

     You really think I could be replaced?

                 G

Nah, I come from outer space.

And I'm a classy girl, I'm a hold it up,

                      Am

You full of something but it ain't love.

                    C

And what we got is straight overdue,

                  G

Go find somebody new.

                 G

Bridge 1   You can buy me diamond earrings

                      Am   C   G

And de - ny-ny-ny, ny-ny-ny, de - ny-ny.

But I smell her on your collar

                     Am   C   G

So good - bye-bye-bye, bye-bye-bye.

Chorus 1

```
         N.C.        G                        Am
I know you're lying 'cause your lips are moving,
         C                G
Tell me do you think I'm dumb?
                            Am
I might be young, but I ain't stupid,
         C                G
Talking 'round in circles with your tongue.
                            Am
I gave you bass, you gave me sweet talk,
         C                  G
Saying how I'm your number one.

                                     Am
But I know you're lying 'cause your lips are moving,
         C                G
Baby, don't you know I'm done.
```

Pre-chorus 2   As Pre-chorus 1

Verse 2
```
         G              Am
Hey, baby, don't you bring them tears,
              C               G
'Cause it's   too late, too late, babe, oh.
                     Am
You only love me when you're here,
             C                   G
You're so   two-faced, two-faced, babe, oh.
```

Bridge 2   As Bridge 1

Chorus 2   As Chorus 1

Pre-chorus 3   As Pre-chorus 1

Chorus 3

N.C.
I know you're lying 'cause your lips are moving,

Tell me do you think I'm dumb?

          G   **Am**
I might be young, but I ain't stupid,

C
Talking 'round in circles with your tongue.

          G   **Am**
I gave you bass, you gave me sweet talk,

C   **G**
Saying how I'm your number one.

                       Am
But I know you're lying 'cause your lips are moving,

C   **N.C.**
Baby, don't you know I'm done.

Photograph

Words & Music by Ed Sheeran & John McDaid

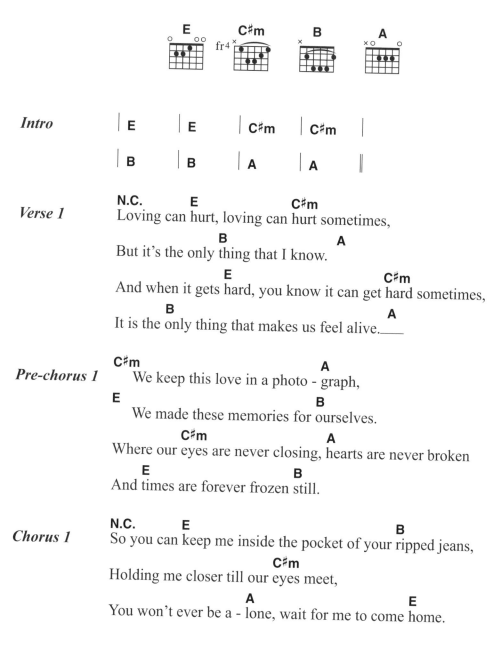

Intro

| E | E | C♯m | C♯m |

| B | B | A | A |

Verse 1

   N.C.   E   C♯m
Loving can hurt, loving can hurt sometimes,

               B   A
But it's the only thing that I know.

                 E   C♯m
And when it gets hard, you know it can get hard sometimes,

               B   A
It is the only thing that makes us feel alive.____

Pre-chorus 1

C♯m   A
   We keep this love in a photo - graph,

E   B
   We made these memories for ourselves.

            C♯m   A
Where our eyes are never closing, hearts are never broken

         E   B
And times are forever frozen still.

Chorus 1

   N.C.   E   B
So you can keep me inside the pocket of your ripped jeans,

                  C♯m
Holding me closer till our eyes meet,

                A   E
You won't ever be a - lone, wait for me to come home.

Verse 2	N.C. E C♯m

Verse 2

          N.C.   E   C♯m
Loving can heal, loving can mend your soul
              B   A
And it's the only thing that I know, know.
                        E   C♯m
I swear it will get easier, remember that with every piece of you,
              B   A
And it's the only thing we take with us when we die.

Pre-chorus 2   As Pre-chorus 1

Chorus 2

          N.C.   E   B
So you can keep me inside the pocket of your ripped jeans,
                         C♯m
Holding me closer till our eyes meet,
                      A
You won't ever be a - lone.
               E   B
And if you hurt me, that's okay baby, only words bleed.
                         C♯m
Inside these pages you just hold me
                         A   C♯m
And I won't ever let you go, wait for me to come home,
                      A
Wait for me to come home,
                      E
Wait for me to come home,
                      B
Wait for me to come home, ooh.

Chorus 3

```
       (B)     E                                                    B
       You can fit me inside the necklace you got when you were sixteen,
                                 C♯m
       Next to your heartbeat where I should be,
                                 A
       Keep it deep within your soul.
                      E                              B
       And if you hurt me, well, that's okay baby, only words bleed,
                          C♯m
       Inside these pages you just hold me
                                 A
       And I won't ever let you go.
```

Chorus 4

```
       (A)              E                          B
       And when I'm a - way, I will remember how you kissed me
                              C♯m
       Under the lamp post back on Sixth Street,
                                    A      N.C.
       Hearing you whisper through the phone,    "Wait for me to come home."
```

Love Me Like You Do

Words & Music by Savan Kotecha, Max Martin, Ilya, Ali Payami & Tove Lo

Chord diagrams: Ab (fr4), Cm7 (fr3), Fm7, Db, Eb (fr3), Ebsus4

Intro

| Ab | Cm7 | Fm7 | Fm7 |

| Db | Eb | Fm7 | Fm7 |

Verse 1

(Fm7)　　Ab
You're the light, you're the night,
　　　　　Cm7
You're the colour of my blood.
　　　　　Fm7
You're the cure, you're the pain,
　　　　　　　　　　　　Db
You're the only thing I wanna touch.
　　　　Eb　　　　　　　　　　Fm7
Never knew that it could mean so much, so much.

Verse 2

(Fm7)　　Ab
You're the fear, I don't care,
　　　　　Cm7
'Cause I've never been so high.
　　　　Fm7
Follow me through the dark,
　　　　　　　　　　　Db
Let me take you past our satel - lites.
　　　　Eb　　　　　　　　　　Fm7
You can see the world you brought to life, to life.

Chorus 1

　　　　　　Ab　　　　　　　　　　　Cm7
So, love me like you do, lo-lo-love me like you do,
Fm7　　　　　　　　　　　Db
Love me like you do, lo-lo-love me like you do.
Bbm　　　　　　　　　　Fm7
Touch me like you do, to-to-touch me like you do,
Ebsus4　　　　Eb
　　What are you waiting for?

Verse 3

(E♭)   A♭
Fading in, fading out,

      Cm⁷
On the edge of paradise.

     Fm⁷
Every inch of your skin

          D♭
Is a holy grail I've got to find.

   E♭   Fm⁷
Only you can set my heart on fire, on fire.

Bridge 1

(Fm⁷)   A♭   Cm⁷
Yeah, I'll let you set the pace_____

     Fm⁷
'Cause I'm not thinking straight,

    D♭   E♭   Fm⁷
My head's spinning around I can't see clear no more.

What are you waiting for?

Chorus 2   As Chorus 1

Chorus 3   As Chorus 1

Link | A♭ | Cm⁷ | Fm⁷ | Fm⁷   ‖

Bridge 2   As Bridge 1

Chorus 4   As Chorus 1

Chorus 5   As Chorus 1

Outro | A♭ | Cm⁷ | Fm⁷ | Fm⁷   ‖

Ship To Wreck

Words & Music by Florence Welch & Thomas Hull

Am   F   Dm   C   G

Intro

‖: Am | F | Dm | Am :‖

Verse 1

Am   F   Dm   Am
Don't touch the sleeping pills, they mess with my head,

F   Dm   Am
Dredging the great white sharks, swimming in the bed.

F   Dm   Am
And here comes a killer whale to sing me to sleep,

F   Dm   Am
Thrashing the covers off, it has me by it's teeth.

Pre-chorus 1

C   Dm   Am   F
And oh, my love remind me, what was it that I said?

C   Dm   Am   F
I can't help but pull the earth around me, to make my bed.

C   Dm   Am   F
And oh, my love remind me, what was it that I did?

C   Dm
Did I drink too much, am I losing touch,

Am   F
Did I build a ship to wreck?

Chorus 1

Am   F   Dm   Am   F
To wreck,___ to wreck,___ to wreck,___

Dm   Am
Did I build this ship to wreck?

Verse 2

```
Am              F           Dm              Am
What's with the long face, or    do you want more?
                F            Dm              Am
Thousands of red-eyed mice,    scratching at the door.
                F
Don't let the curtain catch you,
Dm                              Am
   'Cause you've been here be - fore,
                F
The chair is an island darling,
Dm                        Am
   You can't touch the floor.
```

Pre-chorus 2   As Pre-chorus 1

Chorus 2   As Chorus 1

Interlude

```
Am     F        Dm      Am
   Ooh, oh, ooh, oh, ooh, oh.
       F        Dm      Am
Ooh, oh, ooh, oh, ooh, oh.
```

Bridge

```
(Am)        F           G                   Am
And good God, under starry skies we are lost,
       F
And into the breach we got tossed,
        G               Am
And the water's coming in    fast.
```

Pre-chorus 3   As Pre-chorus 1

Chorus 3

```
     Am    F    Dm    Am              F
To wreck,___ to wreck,___ to wreck,___
        Dm              Am
Did I build this ship to wreck?
     Am    F    Dm    Am              F
To wreck,___ to wreck,___ to wreck,___
        Dm              Am
Did I build this ship to wreck?
```

See You Again

Words & Music by Justin Franks, Cameron Thomaz, Charlie Puth & Andrew Cedar

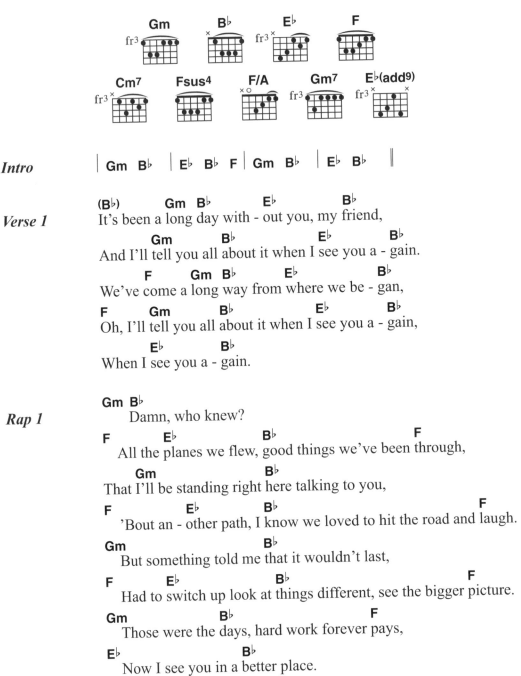

Intro | Gm B♭ | E♭ B♭ F | Gm B♭ | E♭ B♭ ‖

Verse 1

(B♭) Gm B♭   E♭   B♭
It's been a long day with - out you, my friend,
   Gm   B♭   E♭   B♭
And I'll tell you all about it when I see you a - gain.
    F Gm B♭ E♭   B♭
We've come a long way from where we be - gan,
F Gm   B♭   E♭   B♭
Oh, I'll tell you all about it when I see you a - gain,
    E♭   B♭
When I see you a - gain.

Rap 1

 Gm B♭
 Damn, who knew?
F E♭   B♭   F
All the planes we flew, good things we've been through,
 Gm   B♭
That I'll be standing right here talking to you,
F E♭   B♭   F
'Bout an - other path, I know we loved to hit the road and laugh.
Gm   B♭
But something told me that it wouldn't last,
F E♭   B♭   F
Had to switch up look at things different, see the bigger picture.
Gm   B♭   F
Those were the days, hard work forever pays,
E♭   B♭
Now I see you in a better place.

Chorus 1

Gm Bb   Eb
  Ah. How can we not talk about family

Bb
When family's all that we got?

F Gm   Bb
  Everything I went through you were standing there by my side,

F Eb   Bb
  And now you gon' be with me for the last ride.

Verse 2 As Verse 1

Link

N.C. Gm Bb F Eb   Bb
Ah-ah, oh - oh, ah-ah, oh, oh-oh-oh-oh.

    F Gm Bb   F Eb   Bb
Ooh,__ ooh,__ ooh,__ ooh, ooh.__

Rap 2

Gm Bb F   Eb   Bb
  First you both go out your way and the vibe is feeling strong,

F   Gm   Bb
And what's small turn to a friendship, a friendship turn to a bond.

F Eb   Bb
And that bond will never be broken, the love will never get lost,

Gm Bb F   Eb
  And when brotherhood come first,

    Bb
Then the line will never be crossed.

F Eb   Bb
  Esta - blished it on our own, when that line had to be drawn,

F Eb   Bb
And that line is what we reach, so re - member me when I'm gone.

Chorus 2

Gm Bb   Eb
  How can we not talk about family

Bb
When family's all that we got?

F Gm   Bb
  Everything I went through you were standing there by my side,

F Eb   Bb
  And now you gon' be with me for the last ride.

53

Bridge

(B♭)   Cm7 B♭   Fsus4
So let the light guide your way, yeah,

Cm7   B♭   Fsus4
   Hold every memory as you go.

Gm   Cm7   B♭   F/A Gm7 F   E♭(add9)
   And every road you take will al - ways lead you home, home.

Verse 3

(E♭(add9)) Gm B♭   E♭   B♭
It's been a long day with - out you, my friend,

        Gm   B♭   E♭   B♭
And I'll tell you all about it when I see you a - gain.

          Gm B♭   E♭   B♭
We've come a long way from where we be - gan,

F   Gm   B♭   E♭   B♭
Oh, I'll tell you all about it when I see you a - gain,

      E♭   B♭
When I see you a - gain.

Outro

(E♭(add9)) Gm B♭ F   E♭   B♭
Ah-ah,   oh - oh, ah-ah, oh, oh-oh-oh-oh.

      F Gm B♭   F E♭   B♭
Ooh,___ ooh,___ ooh,___ ooh, ooh.___

      Gm B♭ F   E♭   B♭
Ah-ah, oh - oh, ah-ah, oh, oh-oh-oh-oh.

      F Gm B♭   F E♭   B♭
Ooh,___ ooh,___ ooh,___ ooh, ooh.___

Speed Of Light

Words & Music by Bruce Dickinson & Adrian Smith

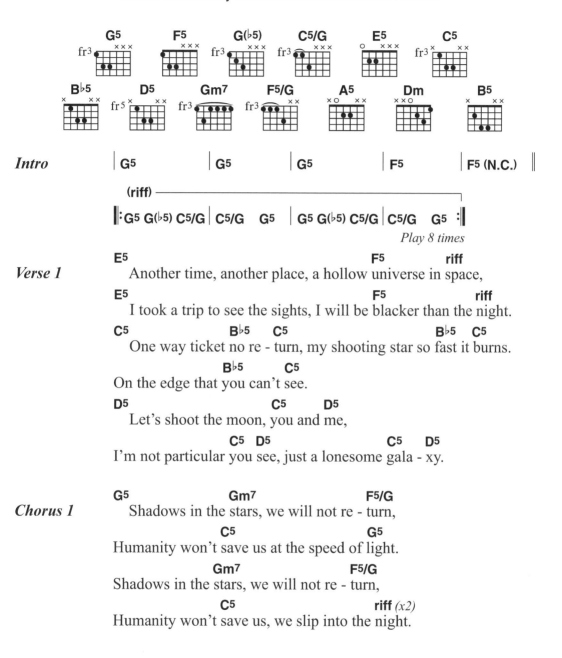

Intro | G5 | G5 | G5 | F5 | F5 (N.C.) ‖

(riff) _____

‖: G5 G(♭5) C5/G | C5/G   G5 | G5 G(♭5) C5/G | C5/G   G5 :‖

Play 8 times

Verse 1

  E5   F5   riff
Another time, another place, a hollow universe in space,

  E5   F5   riff
I took a trip to see the sights, I will be blacker than the night.

  C5   B♭5 C5   B♭5 C5
One way ticket no re - turn, my shooting star so fast it burns.

                    B♭5   C5
On the edge that you can't see.

  D5   C5   D5
Let's shoot the moon, you and me,

                  C5 D5   C5 D5
I'm not particular you see, just a lonesome gala - xy.

Chorus 1

  G5   Gm7   F5/G
Shadows in the stars, we will not re - turn,

                  C5   G5
Humanity won't save us at the speed of light.

                  Gm7   F5/G
Shadows in the stars, we will not re - turn,

                  C5   riff *(x2)*
Humanity won't save us, we slip into the night.

Verse 2

E5   F5   **riff**

I'll say a mass for you and wave shooting plasma from my grave

E5   F5   **riff**

Event horizon lost in space, running in a human race.

C5   B♭5   C5

I don't know where I don't know why

             B♭5   C5

But somehow back in time a - gain,

         B♭5   C5

I'm on the edge that you can't see.

D5   C5   D5

I'm not particular at   night

        C5   D5   C5   D5

A single particle of   me you won't be tracking me by   sight.

Chorus 2

G5   Gm7   F5/G

Shadows in the stars, we will not re - turn,

       C5   G5

Humanity won't save us at the speed of light.

    Gm7   F5/G

Shadows in the stars, we will not re - turn,

       C5   (A5)

Humanity won't save us, we slip into the night.

Guitar solo 1

| ‖: A5 | A5 | G5 | G5 | |
| A5 | A5 | Dm | G5 | :‖ |

Guitar solo 2

| ‖: B5 | B5 | A5 | A5 | |
| B5 | B5 | E5 | A5 | :‖ |

Link

C5	C5	B♭5	C5	C5	B♭5
C5	C5	B♭5	C5	C5	
D5	D5	C5	D5	D5	C5
D5	D5	C5	D5	D5	‖

Chorus 3

G5   Gm7   F5/G
Shadows in the stars, we will not re - turn,

           C5   G5
Humanity won't save us at the speed of light.

         Gm7   F5/G
Shadows in the stars, we will not re - turn,

           C5   G5
Humanity won't save us at the speed of light.

Chorus 4

G5   Gm7   F5/G
Shadows in the stars, we will not re - turn,

           C5   G5
Humanity won't save us at the speed of light.

         Gm7   F5/G
Shadows in the stars, we will not re - turn,

           C5   G5   F5
Humanity won't save us at the speed of light,___

            G5
We slip into the night.___

57

Uptown Funk!

Words & Music by Rudy Taylor, Robert Wilson, Lonnie Simmons,
Ronnie Wilson, Mark Ronson, Philip Lawrence, Jeffrey Bhasker,
Peter Hernandez, Charles Wilson, Nicholaus Williams & Devon Gallaspy

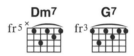

Intro

N.C.
Doh, do-do-do, do-do-do, do-doh.
Dm7
Do-do-do, do-do-do, do-doh.
G7   **Dm7**
Do-do-do, do-do-do, do-doh.
G7
Do-do-do, do-doh.

Verse 1

N.C.
This hit, that ice cold, Michelle Pfeiffer, that white gold.

This one, for them hood girls, them good girls, straight masterpieces.

Stylin', wildin' livin' it up in the city.

Got Chucks on with Saint Laurent, gotta kiss myself I'm so pretty.

Bridge 1

Dm7   **G7**
I'm too hot (hot damn), called a police and a fireman.
Dm7   **G7**
I'm too hot (hot damn), make a dragon wanna retire, man.
Dm7   **G7**
I'm too hot (hot damn), say my name you know who I am.
Dm7   **G7**
I'm too hot (hot damn), am I bad 'bout that money, break it down.

Pre-chorus 1   Girls hit your hallelujah (whoo).

Girls hit your hallelujah (whoo).

Girls hit your hallelujah (whoo).

'Cause Up - town Funk gon' give it to you.

★ = root notes only   **D***   **D♯***   **E***
'Cause Up - town Funk gon' give it to you.
F*   **F♯***   **G***   **G♯***
   'Cause Up - town Funk gon' give it to you.
A*   **A♯***   **B***   **C***   **C♯***
   Satur - day night and we're in the spot,
D*   **N.C.**
Don't   believe me, just watch. (Come on).

Chorus 1
Dm⁷   **G⁷**   **Dm⁷**
(Doh, do-do-do, do-do-do, do-doh.)
G⁷
Don't believe me, just watch.
Dm⁷   **G⁷**   **Dm⁷**
(Doh, do-do-do, do-do-do, do-doh.)
G⁷
Don't believe me, just watch.
N.C.
Don't believe me, just watch.

Don't believe me, just watch.

Don't believe me, just watch.

Hey, hey, hey, oh.

Verse 2
Dm⁷ N.C.
Stop,   wait a minute, fill my cup put some liquor in it.

Take a sip, sign a check, Julio, get the stretch.

Ride to Harlem, Hollywood, Jackson, Mississippi.

If we show up, we gonna show out smoother than a fresh jar o' Skippy.

Bridge 2   As Bridge 1

59

Chorus 2   As Chorus 1

Verse 3
Dm⁷
(Doh, do-do-do, do-do-do, do-doh.)
              G⁷
Before we leave,   let me tell y'all a lil' something.
Dm⁷   G⁷
Uptown Funk you up, Uptown Funk you up.
Dm⁷   G⁷
Uptown Funk you up, Uptown Funk you up, uh.
        Dm⁷   G⁷
I said Uptown Funk you up, Uptown Funk you up,
Dm⁷   G⁷
Uptown Funk you up, Uptown Funk you up.

Verse 4
(G⁷)   Dm⁷   G⁷
Come on, dance, jump on it, if you sexy then flaunt it.
        Dm⁷   G⁷
If you freaky then own it, don't brag about it, come show me.
        Dm⁷   G⁷
Come on, dance, jump on it, if you sexy then flaunt it.
        Dm⁷
Well it's Saturday night and we're in the spot,
G⁷
Don't believe me, just watch. (Come on).

Chorus 3   As Chorus 1

Outro
Dm⁷   G⁷
Uptown Funk you up, Uptown Funk you up.
Dm⁷   G⁷
Uptown Funk you up, Uptown Funk you up.
Dm⁷   G⁷
Uptown Funk you up, Uptown Funk you up.
Dm⁷   G⁷
Uptown Funk you up, Uptown Funk you up.
Dm⁷   G⁷
Uptown Funk you up, Uptown Funk you up.
Dm⁷   G⁷
Uptown Funk you up, Uptown Funk you up.
Dm⁷   G⁷
Uptown Funk you up, Uptown Funk you up.
Dm⁷
Uptown Funk you up.

Writing's On The Wall

Words & Music by James Napier & Sam Smith

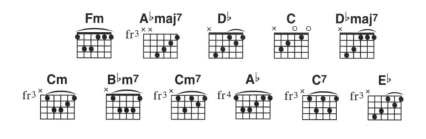

Intro	| **Fm** | **A♭maj7** | **Fm** | **A♭maj7** |	

Verse 1

    Fm   **A♭maj7**
I've been here be - fore

    Fm   **A♭maj7**
But always hit the floor.

        D♭   **C**
I've spent a lifetime running and I always get away,

        D♭   **C**
But with you I'm feeling something that makes me want to stay.

Verse 2

    Fm   **A♭maj7**
I'm prepared for this,

    Fm   **A♭maj7**
I never shoot to miss.

        D♭
But I feel like a storm is coming,

        C
If I'm gonna make it through the day

        D♭
Then there's no more use in running

        C
This is something I gotta face.

Chorus 1

Fm   A♭maj7 D♭maj7
  If I risk it   all

Fm   A♭   C7
  Could you break my fall?

           Fm   E♭
How do I live? How do I breathe?

                 D♭   E♭
When you're not here I'm suffocat - ing.

           Fm   E♭
I want to feel love run through my blood,

      D♭   Cm
Tell me is this where I give it all up?

     B♭m7   Cm7 C7
For you, I have to risk it all,

N.C.   Fm   A♭maj7
  'Cause the writing's on the wall.

Verse 3

Fm   A♭maj7
  A million shards of glass

Fm   A♭maj7
  That haunt me from my past.

        D♭
As the stars begin to gather

        C
And the light begins to fade,

        D♭
When all hope begins to shatter

        C
Know that I won't be afraid.

Chorus 2

Fm   A♭maj7 D♭maj7
  If I risk it   all

Fm   A♭   C7
  Could you break my fall?

           Fm   E♭
How do I live? How do I breathe?

                 D♭   E♭
When you're not here I'm suffocat - ing.

cont.

        Fm   **E♭**
I want to feel love run through my blood,

       D♭   **Cm**
Tell me is this where I give it all up?

   B♭m⁷   **Cm⁷** **C⁷**
For you, I have to risk it all,

N.C.   **Fm**
  'Cause the writing's on the wall.

A♭maj⁷   **Fm**   **A♭maj⁷**
  The writing's on the wall.

Link | **D♭** | **C** | **D♭** | **C**   ‖

Chorus 3

      Fm   **E♭**
How do I live? How do I breathe?

         D♭   **E♭**
When you're not here I'm suffocat - ing.

        Fm   **E♭**
I want to feel love run through my blood,

       D♭   **Cm**
Tell me is this where I give it all up?

        Fm   **E♭**
How do I live? How do I breathe?

         D♭   **E♭**
When you're not here I'm suffocat - ing.

        Fm   **E♭**
I want to feel love run through my blood,

       D♭   **Cm**
Tell me is this where I give it all up?

   B♭m⁷   **Cm⁷** **C⁷**
For you, I have to risk it all,

N.C.   **Fm**
  'Cause the writing's on the wall.

1 2 3 4 5 6 7 8 9

Whatever you want...

Music Sales publishes the very best in printed music for rock & pop, film music, jazz, blues, country and classical as well as songs from all the great stage musicals.

Many of our practical publications come with helpful CDs or exclusive download links to music files for backing tracks and other audio extras.

We also publish a range of tuition titles, books for audition use and book+DVD master classes that let you learn from the world's greatest performers.

So, whatever you want, **Music Sales has it.**

Just visit your local music shop and ask to see our huge range of music in print.

In case of difficulty, contact marketing@musicsales.co.uk